Dedication:

To Pauline

A Visitor Comes to Town

Charles Coulson

A Visitor Comes to Town

Onwards and Upwards Publications, Berkeley House,
11 Nightingale Crescent, West Horsley, Surrey KT24 6PD

www.onwardsandupwards.org

ISBN: 978-1-907509-53-7

Illustrations: Bob Bond
Graphic design: Leah-Maarit
Printed in the UK

1

I was awake, hot with sweat. The angel had returned.

It had been the same dream in the same place. In the dream, a mysterious figure was speaking to a woman.

"I am the angel Gabriel," he said. "Do not be afraid, Mary. You will have a son and give him the name of Jesus. He will be God's son."

His face was a white light and he spoke in a low voice.

"Be ready."

Now I lay in the darkness. Who could I tell? My sister Susanna! I couldn't tell my father or mother; they would just think I was mad. I was afraid to go to sleep because I knew the angel would be waiting. Why did I need to be ready? Why was the birth of a baby my business? Even the Son of God!

By the way, my name is Daniel. My father, Jacob, owns an inn in Bethlehem. It is always busy. We have visitors from all over the country, many of whom are merchants with goods to trade. There are customers from the town, including Roman soldiers when they are off duty. I help out in the stables. The travellers' donkeys, horses, and sometimes camels, need to be fed and watered. My sister works with our mother, Naomi, in the kitchen. We both help with serving food and drink. It is hard, tiring work. But I'm still afraid to go to sleep because of the angel.

"A census, a census," my father shouted. "The Emperor wants to count everyone in the Roman Empire."

Well, all the men.

And how is he going to achieve this? Very simply by everyone registering in the town of their birth.

All the talk was about the census. More taxes to run the Roman Empire. But preparations had to be made because, as Father said, "Business is business." The stables were cleaned out, and more stalls were built. Extra food and straw was ordered and stored in the outhouses. My mother and sister squeezed more beds into the rooms and bought fresh linen covers. They also checked to make sure we had enough food stocks to feed the expected rush of visitors. I didn't have time to dream for the next few weeks.

Bang! Bang!

"Open up! Come on, get a move on!"

Father rushed downstairs and flung open the door. A centurion and several soldiers marched into the inn. They were followed by two men in togas. One was fat and old, the other younger and thinner.

"Quintus and Marcus," said the centurion, pointing at the two figures. "They are here to record the census and will be staying here."

He turned and marched out followed by the soldiers.

"We want the best room in the house. We will need space for our work. We are hungry and tired; have food sent to our room immediately," demanded Quintus, the fat one.

In the middle of the afternoon Marcus came down to arrange their scrolls, pens and ink on a desk in a small room beside the kitchen. The counting began the next day. That night the angel was back.

My father was the first to have his name on the census because he had been born in Bethlehem. A queue began to form across the main room, out of the door and into the dusty road. Susanna and I were kept busy taking drinks and snacks to those patiently waiting to register. At noon the scribes put down their pens and went to eat and rest for an hour.

I took my sister to a quiet corner of the stable yard. I told her about the angel.

"You've dreamed about an angel having a baby?" she shrieked. "You must be mad!"

"Shh, keep your voice down," I hissed. "I couldn't tell mother and father because they would think I was silly. And it's the young woman who's going to have the baby, not the angel."

"Why are you to get ready? When is the baby due? Where is it to be born?" Susanna fired off the questions.

To which I replied, "I don't know."

"We will have to watch for the unusual," Susanna said, "the census for a start!"

It was agreed nothing should be said to our parents; we would watch and listen for any small clue, to try to act as normally as possible and to meet every evening to report our discoveries.

Nothing happened. The dream stopped. We met every evening, but apart from the inn being crammed to the rafters there was nothing to report. Until late one evening a young man came into the inn.

"My name is Joseph," he told my father. "I am looking for lodgings. I have tried all the other inns in town but they are all full. You are my last hope. My wife is due to give birth very soon. She needs a place to rest."

"I'm sorry, Joseph, but we are full due to the census," replied my father.

"I had to come because of the census. I was born in Bethlehem."

"They could stay in the stable. There is an empty stall with a manger. The straw is fresh, and it would be warm." I suddenly found myself speaking without knowing if it was true.

"Thank you," said Joseph.

"I will fetch a lamp and show you the way," I answered. My father was busy with customers and did not notice our conversation.

"Is that all? Is that why you are supposed to be ready?" Susanna muttered when I told her later.

"Well, in the dream there was a young woman who was going to have a baby."

"Yes, but he was to be the son of God. He would be born in a palace not a cramped smelly stable," my sister argued.

I was sitting on the front step. The black sky was filled with millions of stars. The inn was quiet. I was waiting. I was ready. At first I could see yellow lamp light dancing down the road. I heard the sound of shuffling sandals. Out of the shadows came a group of shepherds.

"Where is the Saviour, the Messiah?" the leader asked. "The angels told us to come into town and we would find him in a stable. 'Be ready!' they said."

"I don't know anything about a Saviour, but there is a young woman in the stable who is close to giving birth. Go and have a look, but be quiet."

The youngest shepherd was finishing carving a lamb from wood. "It's a present," he explained.

The stable was as bright as daylight, but the yard was in darkness. I stood outside.

"I hope he likes my present," Reuben grinned as he came out of the stable. He was followed by the other shepherds. They were singing. I thought they would wake up the whole town, not just the inn, but no one opened a window, no lamps were lit. The little town slept peacefully.

I told my sister after breakfast. I couldn't wait.

"Shepherds in the stable! Angels! A baby! The Messiah! I'm going to have a look!"

"No, the baby is probably asleep, and the parents need peace and quiet too. A guest is leaving this morning. When I fetch his horse I'll check."

Later I said, "A blanket has been hung like a curtain to hide the stall. I couldn't see anything." She was disappointed.

If the shepherds were strange night visitors, the next were magnificent.

The inn was quiet; the scribes had gone; the census was completed. The weather was humid and the air crackled; a storm was brewing. I stood on the front step gazing at the sky. One bright star shone over the town, over the inn, casting a silvery light.

A camel coughed... A camel train filled the road. The first three were made to kneel, and three men dismounted. I had never seen robes so rich, in rainbow colours. The colours merged with movement. Signs and symbols flashed and glittered.

"Our journey ends, Melchior and Balthazar," said the first.

"A strange palace for a king, Caspar," replied the second.

"The star has confirmed our calculations," added the third.

Caspar looked at me with piercing eyes. "Where will we find the king?"

"Not here. King Herod lives in his palace," I replied.

"We have come to worship the new born king. The King of the Jews! He was to be born in Bethlehem. We have followed his star from the east," said Melchior.

Without thinking I blurted out, "There was a baby born in the stable behind the inn. Perhaps he is the one." The three men stared silently. "Follow me."

The yard was dark, but daylight filled the stable. The magnificently robed visitors entered solemnly, carrying gifts in jewelled caskets.

It was a short visit. I decided not to tell Susanna; shepherds had been difficult, never mind Magi! The storm began as the last camel turned the corner of the road.

* * * * *

The next dream was urgent. The message was, "Escape to Egypt!"

News travels fast. King Herod was angry - *very* angry. His throne was in danger. A new king had been born.

"All new baby boys are to be killed," a customer was telling my father as I walked through the inn.

Be ready!

The Angel!

The Shepherds!

The Magi!

The King was in the stable!

"Watch for soldiers," I shouted to Susanna as I raced across the yard.

"Why?"

"Just do it!"

It was dim in the stable. The curtain was hanging to one side. A young couple gazed into a manger. A baby boy gazed upwards.

"You must leave now. Soldiers are searching with orders to kill all baby boys. Take this donkey. Leave now. Escape to Egypt. GO!"

The young woman was lifted onto the donkey. The baby, wrapped in a shawl was put in her arms. Their few possessions were stuffed into a leather bag. The man led the way across the yard and out by a side entrance.

Susanna rushed across the yard.

"SOLDIERS!"

Her eyes were wide with fright. The sound of smashing furniture came from the inn. A group clattered into the stable.

We flattened ourselves against the wall. Swords slashed at saddle bags, sliced through leather harnesses and stabbed through sacks of feed and straw. The manger was destroyed with one savage blow. Satisfied there was nothing, they roared out, the lust for destruction in their blood.

We breathed again. Susanna picked up Reuben's wooden lamb.

My friends call me Fish because I spend all my spare time at the lake. It is a very large lake. People call it a sea, the Sea of Galilee. You can't see the other side, even on a sunny day; I've no idea how far it is from end to end. But I know good places to fish.

I had set off early with five small flat loaves baked by my mother. I needed fish to make a meal, cooked on hot stones placed in a fire. I began where a group of trees shaded the water, but no luck. I waded out to some rocks close to the shore, but the fish were not biting. I caught two small fish from a quiet sandy beach but not enough to make a meal. Perhaps the heat was making the fish swim deeper. Was there going to be a thunderstorm?

I decided to try the cliffs. There was a steep track down to the deep cold water. The fish would be nearer the surface.

I walked up a short slope and stopped. There were thousands and thousands of people sitting on the ground. In front of them a man was speaking. I could not hear the words because I was too far away. I was going fishing.

I had to make a path through the crowd, so I trod carefully between the packed people.

"Mind where you're going!"

"Clumsy boy! You stood on my foot."

"Sorry," I replied, "excuse me!"

Some people were rude; they said I was disturbing them and that they couldn't hear Jesus – Jesus the Teacher. My parents had told me about him, how he travelled around the country with his disciples, teaching people about God, the Kingdom of Heaven and how to live a good life.

Were my mum and dad in the crowd?

Now people were moaning, not just at me, but said they were hungry and had nothing to eat. I was going to hang on to my loaves and fish and when I had caught some more I was going to enjoy a feast.

I continued towards the cliff top. A group of men stood where the track went down to the sea.

"Do you have any food in your bag?" one of them asked.

"Only two fish and five loaves," I replied.

"Take them over to Jesus," the man said.

"Why?"

"He's asking who's got any food?"

Reluctantly I did as I was asked and thought, "So much for my feast!"

Jesus was tall, with kind eyes. I handed over my food. He took it, closed his eyes and said a short prayer. He handed the loaves and fish to his disciples who went into the crowd and gave away my meal! You would never believe what happened. All the people were fed until they could eat no more. No one was left hungry. I watched with my mouth open. How could this happen? Jesus did not forget me. I ate until I was full.

The disciples collected twelve baskets of crumbs. My little picnic had fed five thousand people. It was a miracle!

I always make a good catch when I fish in the deep cold water under the cliff where Jesus turned a meal for one into a feast for five thousand.

My father sows corn for farmers. He scatters the seeds from a cloth bag slung over his shoulder. He was ill with a fever so he sent me to sow the corn.

He said, "You may only be a young boy, David, but your mother and younger brothers and sisters will be hungry if there is no money in the house. I'll tell you what to do...

"Walk slowly up and down the field and scatter the seed carefully. If the seed falls on the path the birds will swoop down to peck it up. The seeds that fall where there are stones will grow up but then die quickly because of the poor soil. Some of the seeds will sprout but will be choked by weeds and thistles. It is important that most of the seeds will fall on good ground so they will grow well in the warmth and rain. The farmer wants a fine harvest."

Did I *really* need to hear all that? I've spent hours watching my father sow seeds, walking up and down, up and down. I could scatter seeds in my sleep. I didn't need any advice. I'm nearly eleven years old.

I worked long hours in the fields. I earned enough money to feed the family. The fever subsided and my father was well.

* * * * *

People were very excited. The Teacher, Jesus, was coming to our town. A huge crowd rushed to meet him. Some wanted to ask questions. Some wanted miracles to heal the sick. But most wanted to listen to his teaching about the Kingdom of Heaven. I was curious. I decided to take a day off from working in the fields to listen to him.

He began to tell a story about a sower. His story was similar to my father's with the birds, stones, thistles and good ground to produce good crops.

The story, Jesus explained, wasn't just about seeds but about the Word of God.

"The seeds on the path are like people who hear the word of God but are soon distracted. The ones among the stones are those who are excited when they hear the word but only believe for a short time and forget to think about God when there are difficulties in their lives. The seeds which are choked by thistles are like people who are busy becoming rich and having an easy life. There are many seeds which fall onto good ground, grow strong and produce a good crop. They are like people who hear the word in their hearts and minds, work to lead useful lives and encourage others to listen to the word of God."

I wonder if Jesus knows a story about sheep?

Charles Coulson

A Visitor Comes to Town

"Excuse me! ... Sorry! ... I just need to... Pardon me! ... Sorry!"

We wormed and squirmed our way between bodies and legs until we were at the front of the crowd. Now we could see and hear Jesus. The disciples were annoyed with us for pushing to the front and told us to go and find our parents. But Jesus, in his quiet way, told them to let us stay and listen. "So what's your name?" he asked, looking right in my eyes.

"David," I replied.

"Sit here by me while I tell everyone a story."

"A man went to build a house. He dug deep down and laid the foundations on rock. In the winter the house was battered by wind and rain. It stood firm. A second man went to build a house. He dug down and laid the foundations on sand. In the winter the house was battered by wind and rain. It was demolished... If you hear my words and put them into practice then your life will be like the man who built his house on the rock.

"A woman lost one of her ten silver coins. She searched all over the house. She swept carefully in all the dusty corners. At last she found the coin. She invited her friends and neighbours to celebrate. When we are like the lost coin because we have done wrong, God will search for us and is glad when he finds us again.

"A man planned a great banquet and invited many guests. On the day of the festivities the guests did not arrive. One was too busy because he had bought a new field; one was going to try the new oxen he had bought to pull a plough; another said he had just got married. The owner of the house was very angry and sent his servants into the streets and alleys of the town to bring the poor, the crippled, the blind and the lame to the banquet. This was done, but there was still room. The servants were told to go out on the roads and country lanes and bring anyone they found to the feast. Those who are too busy now will not enter the Kingdom of God.

"There were ten young girls waiting to meet the bridegroom at a wedding. Five of the girls took lamps but did not bother to check the oil. The other five girls filled their lamps with oil and took spare jars of oil. The bridegroom and his friends were very late. All the girls were tired and fell asleep. In the middle of the night the bridegroom arrived. The girls awoke and began to trim the lamps to make them shine brightly. The foolish girls' lamps were dim because they didn't have enough oil. The girls with oil refused to give any to their foolish friends.

"'Go and find your own,' they said.

"The sensible girls went into the wedding banquet with the bridegroom. When the foolish girls returned they had to stay outside. Be ready to meet the Lord!

"There was once a man who owned a hundred sheep. One day a sheep was lost from the flock. The shepherd left the other ninety nine sheep and went to search for the missing sheep. At last he found it and carried the sheep on his shoulders back to rest of the flock. He invited his friends and neighbours to celebrate. God is like the shepherd. There are celebrations in heaven when one person who has lived badly is sorry and begins to live a good life."

So Jesus *did* know a sheep story!

A Visitor Comes to Town

5

A love story? Jesus was going to tell a love story - all 'holding hands, kissing and sloppy talk'! I put my elbows on my knees and covered my ears with my hands. My sister leaned forward to catch every word.

"A young man lived with his father and older brother on a farm. The young man didn't enjoy looking after the animals or working in the fields. He wanted a life of adventure, to visit new places and - most important - to have fun.

"He went to talk to his father. 'Is it true that when you die all the money from the farm will be equally divided between me and my brother?' he asked.

"'Exactly,' replied his father.

"'I don't want to wait until you die,' the young man said. 'I want my share now. I need the money to travel the world and live my own life.'

"His father agreed to his request and several days later the young man left the farm.

"He travelled to a large city in a different country and began to spend his money. The young man was very generous. He gave parties and expensive gifts to his new friends. In a short time the bags of money were empty, and the young man's fair-weather friends deserted him. He needed a job. Looking after a herd of pigs was the only one he could find. In the day the heat made him sweat, and at night the cold made him shiver. The pigs ate better food than he did! It was hard work.

"He was lonely and began to think of his old home. He made up his mind to go and ask his father to let him work as a farm hand. He knew he had been selfish and had wasted the money and made a mess of his life. His father could not be proud of his son.

"The young man stood on the crest of a small hill and looked down on his father's land. The journey had been long, hot and dusty. In the distance he saw a figure. It was his father.

"'Go quickly! We will celebrate with a party. Bring a new robe and sandals for his feet. My lost son has returned!' exclaimed the young man's father to his servant.

"His son called out, 'I don't deserve a party. I have let you down and have come back to work as a farm labourer.'

"But the young man's father just hugged him.

"The older brother came home after a day's work in the fields. He heard music and laughter.

"'What is going on?' he asked a servant.

"'Your brother has come home. There is a party to celebrate,' he was told.

"'I have worked hard on this farm for years and always did as you asked. Why have a party for my brother, who has squandered your money, just because he came home? I've never had a party,' he said angrily to his father.

"'The party is because I love your brother. I thought he was dead but he is alive. I love you also and you are here all the time to receive my love. You are different people, but I love both my sons,' his father replied gently. 'Come and welcome your brother home.'"

Jesus' words had squeezed through my fingers that covered my face. Love is a hard lesson to learn.

"Who is my neighbour?"

Well, the answer is obvious - the people who live next door, the people across the street and anyone who lives nearby are neighbours. That's the answer I would have given. But I learned about a different neighbour.

My father runs an inn on the road from Jerusalem to Jericho. I am his eldest boy, Seth. My job is working in the stable. I have to look after the horses, donkeys and even camels of guests staying overnight at the inn. I work hard, brushing dust from their coats, feeding them and making sure they have clean drinking water. It is smelly work. If I do a good job, the guests will give me a few small coins in payment. Some think they have paid enough for their accommodation; some are just rude.

A few weeks ago my father took me to hear Jesus, the Teacher. Jesus was with his disciples. A huge crowd of people had come to listen. He taught people by telling parables - stories about how to live a good life, about God and life eternal.

"How do I enter the Kingdom of Heaven?" he had been asked by a man in the crowd.

Jesus asked the man, "What is written in the temple scrolls?"

"Love the Lord your God with all your heart and with all your soul, with all your strength and with all your mind. You must love your neighbour as yourself."

"Well answered!" replied Jesus. "Do as you have said and you will enter the Kingdom of Heaven."

"I do love God, but who is my neighbour?" asked the man

What a silly question!

Jesus told us a parable.

"A man was travelling from Jerusalem to Jericho. He was attacked by robbers. They tore off his clothes and beat him up. They stole his money and left him in a ditch. A priest who was walking along the road saw the injured man. He crossed the road. He didn't stop to help. A short time later another man went down the road. He was a Levite, a temple official. He saw the injured man and, like the priest, he didn't stop the help.

"Later in the day another man travelled down the road. He was a Samaritan. When he saw the injured man in the ditch he went to help. He cleaned the wounds with wine and oil and wrapped them in clean bandages. The injured man could not walk, so the Samaritan put him on his donkey. Further along the road the Samaritan reached an inn. The innkeeper was asked to look after the injured man. The innkeeper was paid for food, accommodation and medical expenses.

"'If you need any more money I will pay on my way back from Jericho,' said the Samaritan."

"Who was a neighbour to the man who was robbed?" Jesus asked.

"The man who helped," replied the man who had first asked the question.

"Go and do the same!" said Jesus.

On the way home I asked my father, "Does the story mean that if we help a person who is injured they become our neighbour?"

"It is a parable to show us how to treat people, whether or not we like them," he explained.

He explained that my neighbours don't just live nearby. Our neighbours are from far and wide.

The work in the stable is still smelly. I am trying to be pleasant to our guests, even those who are rude and don't say thank you.

It's not always easy being a Good Samaritan.

7

Passover: a celebration, a remembrance of the Israelites deliverance from the Egyptians. The city was filling with travellers from far and near. The market traders, the temple stall holders and the innkeepers were expecting business to be brisk and profitable. My father, Daniel, who owns an inn, was making preparations.

He had come to Jerusalem from Bethlehem about thirty years ago with my grandfather and grandmother, Jacob and Naomi. My Aunt Susanna had lived with them a few years before she married a merchant and went to live in Nazareth. Sadly my grandparents are dead, so my father and mother took over the inn.

"Nathan, Miriam, come here!" my father shouted.

We had been idly watching the crowds pass the front door.

"Nathan, go and give the stable a good sweep, please! Miriam I'd like you to go and tidy the spare room upstairs. Your mother is busy in the kitchen and I have to visit the wine merchant."

I had brushed a pile of straw into a heap when I heard Miriam.

"Quick, Nathan, come and look at this!"

I dropped the brush and ran up the outside steps and through the door to the upstairs room. Miriam was leaning out of a front window. She was waving. She was waving to a man riding a donkey! She was not alone in her greetings. Hundreds of people, waving palm branches and shouting, walked behind the man on the donkey.

"Hosanna! Blessed is he who comes in the name of the Lord! Blessed is the king of Israel!"

Beside the donkey walked a dozen men like guards, but they had no weapons. We watched the procession pass.

"Look," said Miriam, and she waved again, "Aunt Susanna and our cousins."

She rushed off to say hello.

"There will be trouble," my father said. "The Roman soldiers are ready."

The next day Miriam, our cousins, Sarah, Simon and I were out in the city and found ourselves by the temple. As usual it was busy with priests, pilgrims and stall holders: the dove sellers and money changers doing brisk business. Suddenly a figure came out of the temple door. It was the donkey man, who we now knew was called Jesus, surrounded by his followers. Coins bounced down the steps as tables were kicked over, and doves flew in clouds over the square as Jesus kicked over tables and smashed open wicker cages.

"This is my father's house and you have made it a den of thieves!" he roared in his furious attack. Soldiers nearby gripped their swords but had no orders to intervene. Jesus cast a dark look at the priests and left the square.

"We have guests in the upstairs room tonight," said father. "Two men, Peter and John, came to ask for it to be prepared for the Passover. Everything is ready, but you youngsters will need to look after our guests - your mother and I will be busy in the kitchen."

"How many guests?" asked Miriam.

"Thirteen," replied my father.

The guests arrived. We did not dare tell Dad that Jesus and his disciples were in the room above his head! When we took the food and wine Jesus asked our names. Sarah told him how they had followed the procession into the city. He had smiled when Simon told him they lived in Nazareth. Miriam said she had heard about the story of the Good Samaritan. I just stood and gawped. He gave us a blessing, and we left them to their Passover meal.

It was a warm night. We sat with our backs against the stable wall and talked. We all agreed the blessing felt like a warm hand resting on your head.

"What trouble can he cause?" asked Sarah. "We followed the procession; everyone was happy and calling him a king."

"But then he threw out the traders of the temple steps. You could see the priests were not happy," said Simon.

"We'd better make sure they have enough bread and wine," said my sister. "Come on, Sarah!"

"He's no King without an army," said Simon.

"And one of his soldiers is running away," I whispered as a figure slunk down the outside steps.

Sarah and Miriam had just told us how they had overheard Jesus talking about bread, wine and betrayal. The door of the room had not quite been closed.

"What about?..." but the rest of Miriam's question was muffled by my hand. Jesus and his disciples were leaving. We followed them to a wooded place called Gethsemane.

Jesus left his disciples and went further on his own. We crouched in a thicket of bushes. Nothing happened. Sarah fell asleep. Jesus returned and found his disciples sleeping too.

"Could you not keep watch for one hour?" he said.

Nothing was going to happen. I signed that we should go home, but suddenly it was all action!

Torches flickered; shadowy figures hurried forward; the heavy tramp of soldiers echoed through the trees. Jesus was surrounded by men with clubs, soldiers with short swords and in the middle the man who had left the inn. Judas stepped forward and greeted Jesus with a kiss and the word, "Rabbi."

There was a brief scuffle.

A sword blade glittered in the moon light. Jesus had been arrested.

The disciples had fled.

We followed the crowd at a discrete distance back to the city.

Jesus was taken to the house of Caiaphas, the high priest. News of the arrest had spread quickly, and a crowd of people filled the courtyard. The excited talk was of a trial, how Jesus had been stirring up trouble with his teaching about God and the Kingdom of Heaven and how the authorities wanted him silenced. He had spoken kindly to us only a few hours ago. We stood nervously and listened. A servant girl from the house pushed her way through the crowd. She spoke to a man near us.

"You were with Jesus," she said.

"I don't know who you mean," he responded.

She said, "This man is one of the disciples."

"I'm not!" was the reply.

"You are from Galilee. I can tell from your accent. You *must* know Jesus," another man said.

"Yes, he..." but my elbow in Miriam's ribs stifled her words.

A cockerel crowed.

The man fled. It was the man Peter, who had arranged the Passover meal.

Jesus was brought into the courtyard bound with rope.

"He says he is the King of the Jews," Caiaphas announced. "Pontius Pilate can decide if he lived or dies."

We ran home.

Mother, Father and Aunt Susanna were angry and shouted about selfishness, thoughtless behaviour and causing worry. All this was mixed with hugs and tears of joy we were home safely. In this confusion we gabbled out the story. The room went quiet.

"Time to go," said father. We hurried out leaving the door wide open.

The crowd was like a monster, eyes focusing upwards, breathing hot air and making the early morning air shimmer. Pilate, dressed in his finest robes, stood on the balcony.

"Do you want me to release the King of the Jews?"

"We want Barabbas," roared the crowd.

It was usual for the Romans to release a prisoner at the time of Passover. Barabbas was in jail for murder.

"What shall I do with Jesus?" Pilate asked.

"Crucify him!" screamed the mob.

(The Romans used crucifixion to keep control of their empire.)

The crowd swayed and heaved as people struggled to find a place to stand. Orders rang out as the palace gates opened. The crowd parted, waves rolling back from a sea shore. A squad of soldiers led by a centurion moved forward. Jesus staggered behind. He was wearing a crown of thorns; blood trickled down his cheek. Blood also soaked his back. He had been flogged. A heavy timber for the cross pressed on his shoulder. Soldiers prodded him forward. The crowd jeered.

Jesus tottered and fell as he approached where we stood watching. A man was hauled out of the crowd and made to carry the timber. Jesus looked and smiled as he struggled to his feet. Our faces were wet with tears. The procession wound its way to Golgotha, the 'Place of the Skull'.

* * * * *

Nails pierced his wrists and feet as the cross on which he hung was hauled upright. A sign was nailed above his head: "King of the Jews".

"If you are the Christ, save yourself! Come down from the cross!" mocked the crowd.

The sky turned black.

We stood for a long time.

Jesus cried out, "I'm thirsty."

A sponge was soaked in wine vinegar and held to his lips on a stick.

He drank.

"It is finished," said Jesus.

He bowed his head and died.

A group of women stood near the cross, one of whom was his mother Mary.

"The world will change," my father said quietly as we walked back to the inn.

A Visitor Comes to Town

"My last week! My last week!"

The sound from his nail-shod sandals echoed his thoughts. How many miles had he marched across the Empire? His last week of service, a few more mundane hours in the garrison, and then... home.

"My last week! My last week!"

Marcus, Roman legionary, with twenty five years to his credit, chanted in his head as he marched at the head of the small troop. His orders were simple: identify trouble-makers and persuade them to be good, using any means necessary. The legionaries had enforced such orders many times to subdue people who resented the rule of Rome. The methods ranged from a mild roughing up to crucifixion (when a particular example needed to be set). Marcus raised his hand, the troop halted and deployed to either side of the road. Marcus led several men through the gate to stand outside the city walls, the West Gate of Jerusalem.

The soldiers scrutinised the passing faces. There were merchants from across the Empire, country folk with fresh produce to sell at the market and pilgrims arriving to celebrate Passover.

It was a tedious job, watching people. Now and then an individual or small group were taken aside, briefly interrogated and left in no doubt that trouble would be swiftly and harshly repressed. The landscape shimmered in the heat; it was difficult to judge distance. Marcus shaded his eyes against the glare. A dust cloud had formed on the horizon - a dust storm caused by the heat, or a marching column. Marcus spoke quietly to a soldier who slipped through the gate, then returned with the rest of the troop. The cloud came nearer. The figures could be glimpsed through the swirling dust.

How many?

Now the soldiers heard shouting.

"My last week..."

One quiet week was about to vanish, thought Marcus, as he adjusted the grip on his short sword.

"Hosanna, Hosanna, hail the King of Jews!"

The shouting was a chant, endlessly repeated, growing louder as the marchers neared the gate - the sound rebounding off the city walls. Palm branches were waved as flags; the column stretched far along the road. At the head of the column rode a man - a man on a donkey.

A king on a donkey?! Ridiculous!

Kings and emperors rode magnificent horses with mounted guards riding close. The donkey man had no armed guards, but a group of men walked close. People rushed forward to lay a carpet of cloaks.

Marcus made a decision: "Let them pass!"

The donkey man, 'the King', rode though the gate. He smiled, but it was not reflected in his brown eyes. The chanting crowd surged through the gate.

Marcus reformed the troop to return to barracks.

"My last week! My last week!" his marching feet chanted in his head.

My last week! Newborn king!

My last week! Newborn king!

Newborn king! Newborn king!

He stumbled and nearly fell. Why had the chant changed? The crowds moved aside at the soldiers tramp. He heard snatches of conversation...

"He is a teacher..."

"...lives a peaceful life..."

"...followers are disciples..."

"...born in Bethlehem..."

Bethlehem. His father, Lurgis, had served in Bethlehem and told a story about a 'newborn king'. It would have been over thirty years ago. The Emperor, Caesar Augustus, had ordered a census for tax purposes and the people had had to register in their town of birth.

"Thousands were on the move," Lurgis had said.

The town had been packed - no spare accommodation, not a room vacant. It had been his father's last week as a soldier and he had wanted a quiet few days. Rumours had indicated that a king had been born, philosophers had come to visit, and Herod had been incandescent with rage. All the soldiers had been ordered out of barracks on a killing spree of baby boys. Lurgis had said there had been strange sights and sounds in the night sky. He had made a show of obeying orders, but with one week to serve, he and his troop had found no baby boys. They had even searched outbuildings and stables.

Newborn king!

King of Jews.!
Newborn king!
King of Jews.!
Tramp, tramp, tramp!
Tramp, tramp, tramp!
Soon be home! Soon be home!
King of Jews!
Newborn king!

The beat of his marching feet echoed the beat of words in his head. Marcus and his troop were on patrol in the city. They would soon reach the Temple. It always thronged with people: priests holding services and preaching, pilgrims who travelled to worship at the holy site, the sick praying for cures, numerous traders and merchants. They set up their stalls and tables on the steps outside the temple building. It was a regular stop on a patrol. The Romans kept a close eye, with so many people mixing together. It was an ideal place for dissent and intrigue to flourish.

The troop turned into the square. The donkey man, 'King of Jews,' stood on the forecourt of the Temple.

"You have turned my father's house into a den of thieves," he shouted.

He kicked over a table, scattering a money changer's coin, which bounced down the steps. Next he broke open a basket containing doves, which were sold for sacrifice. They flew free over the square. Several more stalls were dashed over. Men shouted and cursed. Marcus sensed the soldiers wanted to restore order, but he held them back. The donkey man spotted the soldiers and, with his followers, calmly walked away through the Temple precincts.

Passover was a quiet festival, celebrated behind closed doors. The garrison was not expecting trouble. Marcus had eaten an evening meal and was relaxing with comrades playing dice. A centurion entered and had a brief conversation with Marcus.

Make no noise!

Make no noise!

The troop was lightly armed with swords. They moved up a gentle slope between olive trees ripe for harvesting.

Make no noise!

Make no noise!

Marcus did not want to hear another beat in his head. He scanned the trees on either side for a possible ambush. They had been joined by a group of priests just before they began to climb. He knew the locals called it the Garden of Gethsemane.

A cloud drifted from the moon's face, and its silver light shone into a small clearing. A small group of men stood quietly talking. The soldiers quickly surrounded the men and waited for the signal. A man stepped from among the priests and walked towards the waiting men.

"Rabbi," he said and gently kissed a cheek. There was a brief skirmish. We had arrested the donkey man. A cloud hid the moon.

Chaos followed the arrest. The donkey man was taken to a court of priests for a trial behind closed doors. He was charged with being the Son of Man and for 'blasphemous' teaching about God's kingdom - a crime against God himself. The witnesses brought to testify against the accused made contradictory statements about his guilt or innocence. But the priests were determined. The man had to be silenced and his thoughts and ideas buried and forgotten. He had to die. His fate lay in the hands of Pontius Pilate, the Roman Governor.

The crowd, their feelings and fears inflamed by rumour and speculation, would not listen to Pilate. He thought the prisoner was innocent and should be released. It was, however, tradition that a criminal should be set free at Passover. The crowd screamed for Barabbas, a murderer. Pilate did not want trouble. He passed sentence. Afterwards he asked for a bowl of water and washed his hands of the consequences of his action: death by crucifixion.

It was alleged one of the donkey-man's disciples had been seen near to the court house warming himself by a fire. The man, Peter, had been asked three times if he was a friend of the prisoner. He had made two denials. He had also denied it a third time as a cock had crowed. He had cried and run away in despair. At around the same time, soldiers had found a man hanged in a tree. He was identified as the betrayer in the garden: a man called Judas.

King of Jews!

King of Jews!

Marcus watched as his soldiers made fun of the donkey man. A kingly purple rode had been draped across his shoulders and a thorny crown balanced on his head.

Hail the King!

Hail the King!

The fun was soon over. The robe stripped off, the crown dashed to the floor. The flogging began. Marcus had seen, and taken part, in many beatings before an execution. Today he watched. So much blood in a man's back.

Crucify!

King of Jews!

Crucify!

Crucify!

The donkey man shouldered the bar of his crucifixion cross. Marcus followed - a slow heavy tread.

One more week!

My last week!

King of Jews!

Hosanna!

Trailing the procession was a group of silent women, including the mother of the donkey man.

The crowd lined the city streets, their rhythmic shouts beat time to the march. Soldiers with whips and clubs forced a path through the crowd - a path to Golgotha.

The Place of the Skull.

Thud, thud, thud!

The heavy hammer drove the iron nails through sinew and muscle of the donkey man and two robbers sentenced to crucifixion. Once the bodies had been nailed by wrists and feet to the wood, the crosses were hauled upright with ropes to crash into post holes. A sign which read, "King of the Jews," was nailed to one cross. The death was slow and painful.

The baying crowd melted away, satisfied. The silent group of mourners stood watching and waiting.

Time passed slowly.

The victims moaned and screamed as their strength faded.

The end was sudden.

The sky went black.

The donkey man cried out to his father in heaven.

He died.

The watchers asked permission to take the body for burial. He was taken and gently placed in a stone tomb. A heavy stone was pushed against the entrance.

* * * * *

Marcus marched back to the barracks and took off his uniform for the last time.

Tramp, tramp, tramp!

Marcus walked at a steady pace. He was a civilian, on his way home to Italy. A figure stood waiting where a path joined the road. Marcus was wary. Perhaps others lay ready to spring an ambush. The stranger smiled and offered a friendly greeting. Marcus forgot his fears and was soon telling the stranger his plans for the future. He asked the occasional question, but mostly he listened. At noon they sat in the shade of a tree to rest and eat. It was an unusual meal. Marcus had bread and wine in his bag. The stranger took them, said a prayer, and then offered them back to Marcus to eat and drink. As they continued along the road Marcus told the stranger about his week in Jerusalem. It was late in the day when the two travellers reached the top of a long, slow climb. In the far distance the sky and sea drew a flat horizon. The sun, a crimson ball, was sinking slowly. The road forked left to the port and right to continue along the coast.

"My road is this way," said the stranger.

"Thank you for your company, but I don't know your name," Marcus replied.

The stranger smiled and set off along the path. He walked a short distance, turned and lifted his hand to wave. The evening light shone on his face. His sleeve slipped down his arm. The figure was covered in light as the sun set.

Marcus knew the stranger.

* * * * *

Marcus, his wife, children and grandchildren sat around a long wooden table on the terrace in front of the stone farmhouse. It was hot, but the table was in the cool shade of several oaks. The farmhouse stood on a gently sloping hill. In front was a grove of olive trees; to each side vegetables grew in neat rows; while behind the house on rougher ground grazed sheep and goats; chickens pecked and scratched in the dusty soil. The olives were pressed for oil which was poured into large, double handled, stopped earthen jars. The jars were loaded onto carts packed with straw and sold in the nearby town. Marcus received a good price for his oil; it was in great demand in Rome.

Marcus finished the story. His family sat still. A gentle breeze shook the oak leaves; shadows danced on the table. The silence was broken by his eldest son.

"Why tell us now, today?"

"It is the 25th anniversary of my last week of service. The donkey-man, or Jesus Christ, to give him his rightful name, was a danger to the powerful religious leaders. The crucifixion was to silence him and kill his teaching and ideas. All would be buried and forgotten. He believed in one God, a loving God, a God who forgives those who are sorry for mistakes and a God who promises a new life in heaven after death. Romans believe in many gods. "The Christians, people who believe His words, are now too numerous to count. They are persecuted, beaten, even killed as a sport by lions and gladiators in amphitheatres, but still their numbers grow. The Roman Empire will not last forever. The world will change. But the words of the donkey-man will roll on through all time. We must celebrate his memory."

Marcus broke a piece of bread from a flat loaf. He handed the loaf to his wife who did the same. The loaf passed from hand to hand; even the youngest child broke off a tiny piece. All ate the bread. Marcus drank from a cup of wine. The cup was handed around the table. All drank the wine. He said a prayer.

Marcus smiled...